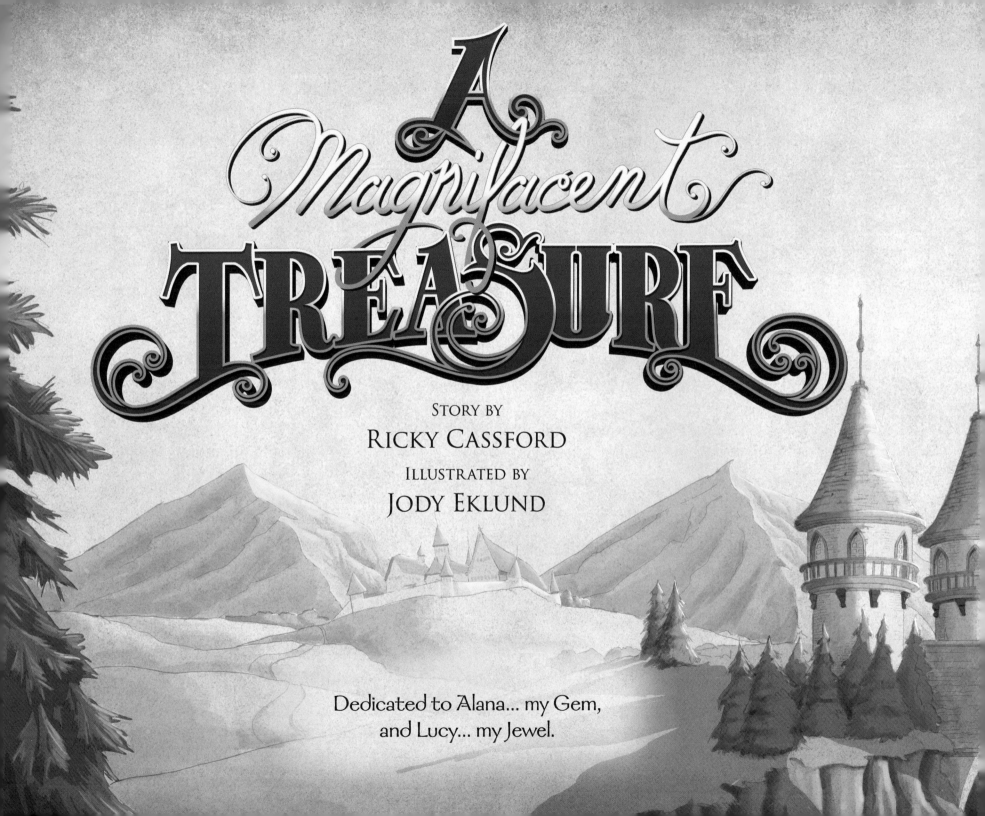

A Magnificent Treasure

STORY BY

RICKY CASSFORD

ILLUSTRATED BY

JODY EKLUND

Dedicated to Alana... my Gem,
and Lucy... my Jewel.

*O*nce upon a time in a faraway land (though a land that seems nearer than far) a young maiden lived high in a tower overlooking the city of her dreams... and though the maiden had everything she needed, the tower was guarded by an enchanted dragon!

While Knights, brave boys, and sometimes-even thugs attempted to claim the maiden as their prize, the dragon continually challenged the boys and decisively won every time. Dragons are well known to be great protectors, and their strength is especially fierce when they are protecting their treasure...

...and as much as these young men, who fought the dragon, sought to set the maiden free she did not, in any way, feel in danger. The maiden instead, felt secure in the dragon's presence. She knew that she was worth more than a pile of gold in the eyes of her protector, and that was all that mattered.

"Good morning my Treasure!" the dragon would call as each day dawned.

And the maiden would reply,

*"Good morning
my Dragon!"*

The maiden loved to talk about the city of her dreams, "Some days it seems far, far away," she would say "and others it seems so close I can reach out and touch it." The dragon would nod and say, "I know."

Whether the maiden was soaking in the sunshine as they soared high over the grass across the meadow of light or clinging tightly to his side as they passed through the valley of shadows, talking about the city always put the maiden in a good mood, and the dragon would often inspire her with tales of opportunities that awaited her in the city.

"Will you come too? When will that day be? How can I even stand the wait?" the maiden asked one day.

"I do not know the answers to everything," said the dragon with a hint of sorrow behind his eyes, "and what I do know I have always tried to teach you. You have always trusted me, and I ask that you keep trusting me until the day appointed that you leave my side."

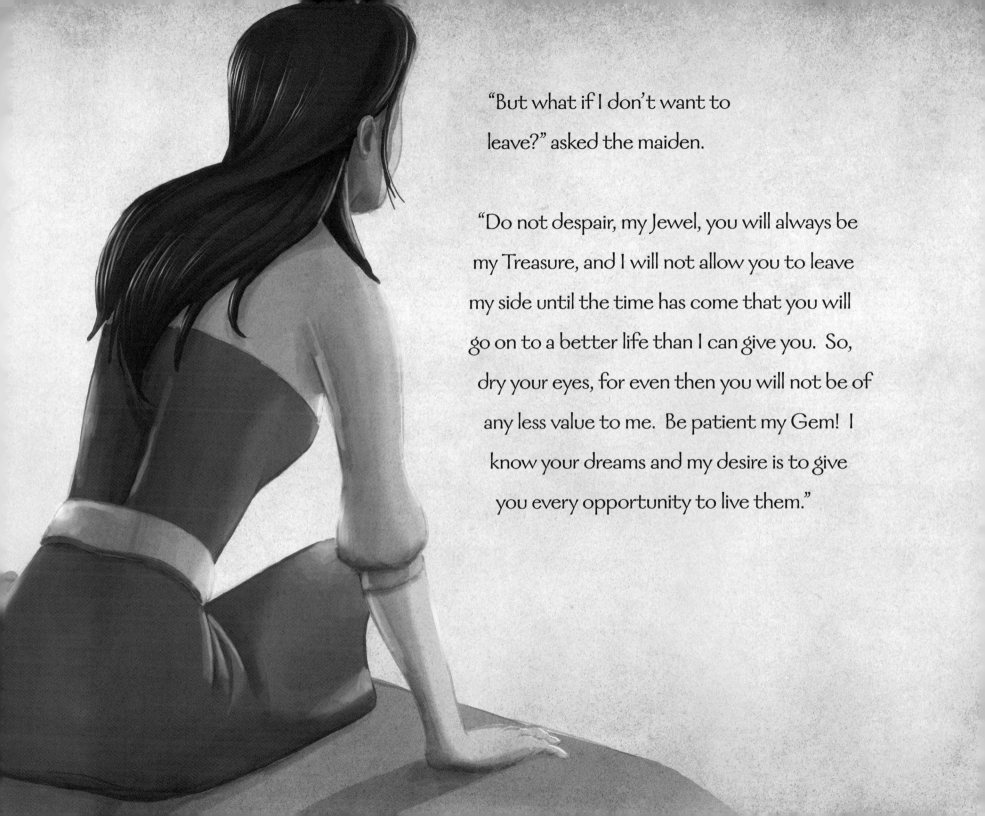

"But what if I don't want to leave?" asked the maiden.

"Do not despair, my Jewel, you will always be my Treasure, and I will not allow you to leave my side until the time has come that you will go on to a better life than I can give you. So, dry your eyes, for even then you will not be of any less value to me. Be patient my Gem! I know your dreams and my desire is to give you every opportunity to live them."

As each day closed

the dragon would say,

"Good night
my Treasure..."

and the maiden would reply,

"Good night my Dragon."

Then a day came when a bold knight saw the maiden, high in her tower, as he was traveling just outside the city. He thought to himself, "I must have her for my own!" Overly confident that he would impress them with his deeds, he gathered fellow knights, friends and neighbors to watch as he displayed his valor.

"Have you come to take my treasure?" asked
the dragon, as the knight approached.

"My name is Sir Johann Bravado! I am the bravest knight in these
lands, and your treasure will be my spoil when I vanquish you!"
shouted back the knight as he moved toward the dragon.

The crowd cheered and Johann Bravado

fought bravely, but in the end, the

dragon threw him back the way he had

come to land amongst the crowd.

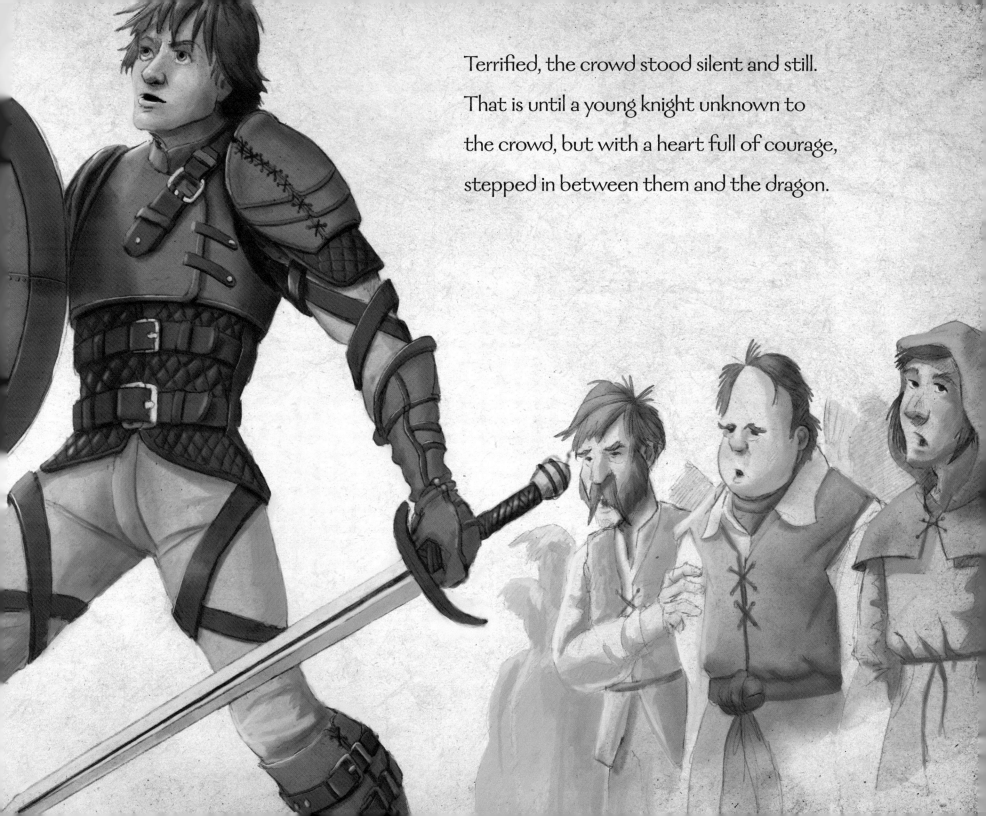

Terrified, the crowd stood silent and still. That is until a young knight unknown to the crowd, but with a heart full of courage, stepped in between them and the dragon.

"You know I have the ability to remove this entire crowd," said the dragon.

"I understand," responded the young knight, with only the slightest waver in his voice, "that is why I have stepped forward to defend them."

"Have you no fear, like the rest?" rumbled the dragon, towering over the knight, "Many have come, none have passed."

"I am afraid," said the knight with his sword at the ready. "But I have learned to focus my fear and knowledge in order to stand strong for what is right."

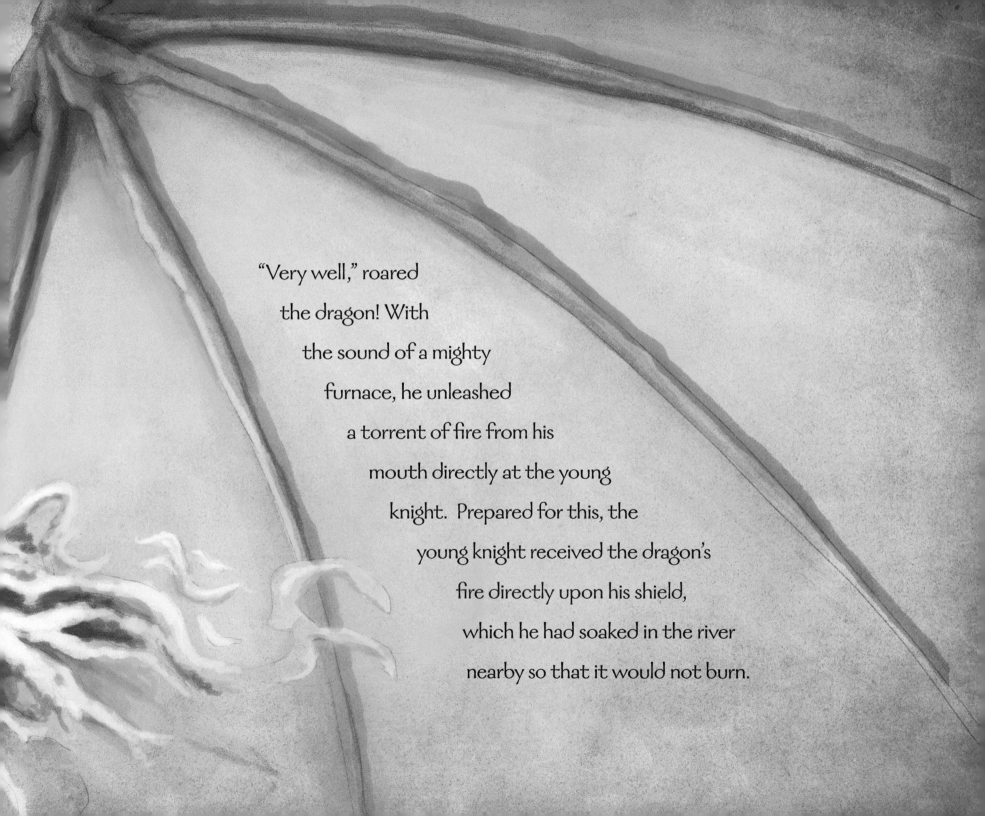

"Very well," roared
the dragon! With
the sound of a mighty
furnace, he unleashed
a torrent of fire from his
mouth directly at the young
knight. Prepared for this, the
young knight received the dragon's
fire directly upon his shield,
which he had soaked in the river
nearby so that it would not burn.

When the flames had stopped, the knight slowly lowered his shield to find the dragon sitting proudly at the gate of his castle. Once the crowd realized that there wasn't to be another battle to enjoy, they slowly and sadly began to return to the city. The young man remained. Realizing he was now alone, the knight lowered his sword, and approached the dragon with care.

"I see that you come to me with courage and respect," said the dragon, "with none of the selfishness of the last night who failed. What is your name? Have you come, now, to take my treasure?"

"My name is Samuel," said the young knight, "and while I have much to learn, my understanding of chivalry is to protect not to take."

"Tell me, young knight, do you think the maiden is beautiful?"

"I think she is the most beautiful maiden that I have ever seen," said the knight. "I have seen her many times, and know that her beauty comes from the inside, and magnificently makes itself known upon her face. Sir, I have seen the way that you treasure her, and I wish to treasure, protect, and cherish her with the rest of my life."

"Is that so?" questioned the dragon.

"So, test me as you will," continued the knight, raising his sword and shield once again, "and see that I am prepared to give all of my strength for her!"

At those words the dragon let out a great roar, and with the sound of mighty rushing winds the dragon began to shrink from his monstrous form. His scales fell, his wings folded back, and with a final burst of light he no longer looked like a dragon. He did, in fact, look like...

...a man.

"Daddy," exclaimed the maiden running from the safety of the castle wall!

"Come here young and noble knight," said the dragon, "and I will explain." With his daughter in his arms, he began to tell the knight a story.

"Many years ago, the King of the land gave me a Magnificent Treasure. He charged me with protecting, providing, and guiding this Treasure into the right hands. In the presence of the King I placed a spell upon myself that would help me, at all costs, to protect this great Treasure until the time should come that one worthy to continue these duties made himself known. Through your valor and sense of honor you have broken that spell. You have proven yourself worthy of this Treasure...

...with my blessing, take my daughter, the greatest
treasure in the land, to the city of her dreams.
Protect her. Provide for her. Serve her for as long
as you live. I pass on my duties willingly, as the
King would have it, into your hands, my son."

So, the maiden and the knight lived, ever
after, seeking to treasure one another greatly,
as the King had always intended.

And still to this day, whenever the

maiden has the chance she'll say,

"Good night
my Dragon,"

and of course the response

will always be,

"Good night
my Treasure!"

CPSIA information can be obtained at www.ICGtesting.com
Printed in the USA
LVIW01n1524231217
560600LV00002B/2